Peter Lancett is c .... airor and film maker. He has wri...in many books, and has just made a feature film, *The Xlitherman*.

Peter now lives in New Zealand and California.

Dark Man

The Dark Trap
by Peter Lancett
illustrated by Jan Pedroietta

Published by Ransom Publishing Ltd.
Radley House, 8 St. Cross Road, Winchester, Hampshire
SO23 9HX
www.ransom.co.uk

ISBN   978 184167 987 7

First published in 2010

Copyright © 2010 Ransom Publishing Ltd.

Dark Man

The Dark Trap

A play

by Peter Lancett

illustrated by Jan Pedroietta

The Dark Trap
The Players

The Dark Man
(189 words)

Narrator
(142 words)

The Old Man
(122 words)

Powerful man
(43 words)

Shadow Master 1
(40 words)

Dying girl
(33 words)

Shadow Master 2
(17 words)

Astrid
(13 words)

Demon
(11 words)

The Dark Trap
The Acts

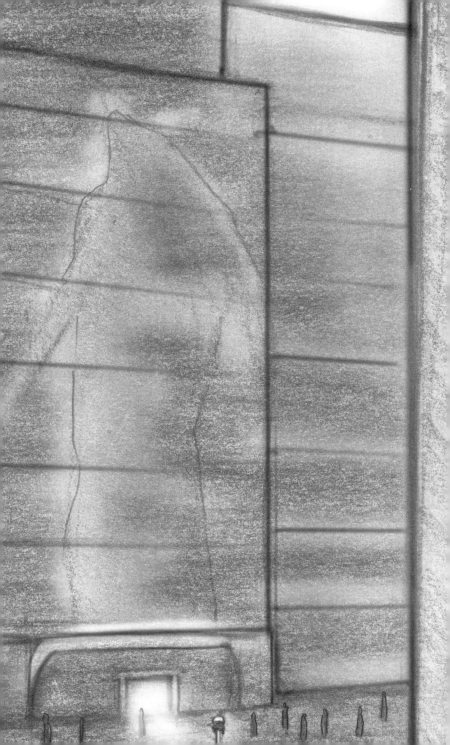

1

Act One:
In the Office

Narrator:
The Dark Man is going to
see a powerful man.

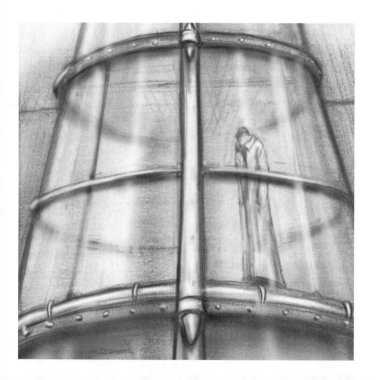

Narrator:
> The Dark Man enters the office of the powerful man.

Powerful man:
> Ah. You have come. I knew that you would. Come in.

The Dark Man:
I am not here to talk to you. I know what you are. I am here to stop you.

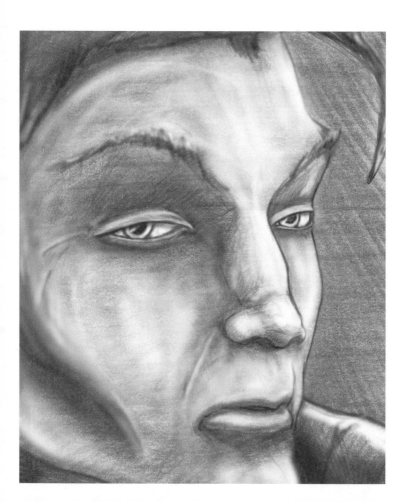

 Powerful man:
So, the Old Man has put
ideas in your head. That is
a pity.

 The Dark Man:
I know that you have a
magic stone. I see it on
your desk.

 Powerful man:
You know nothing! You will
never leave here alive!

11

Narrator:
> The powerful man shows what he really is. A demon.

Powerful man:
> The stone is mine! You must not touch it!

The Dark Man:
> The Old Man wants it, so I am taking it.

Narrator:
The magic stone has made the Dark Man very strong.

The Dark Man:
Go back to the evil place you came from!

Narrator:
The powerful man screams. The Dark Man throws him through the window.

Narrator:
The Dark Man knows that the stone gave him extra strength.

The Dark Man:
This stone has strong magic. I must take it to the Old Man.

2 Act Two:
With the Old Man

Narrator:
The Dark Man has found the Old Man.

The Old Man:
You did well to take the stone. And to kill that demon.

The Dark Man:
The stone gave me the power to do it.

 The Old Man:
Yes, the stone has strong magic.

The Old Man:
> What is making you so
> sad?

The Dark Man:
> You can tell that I am sad?

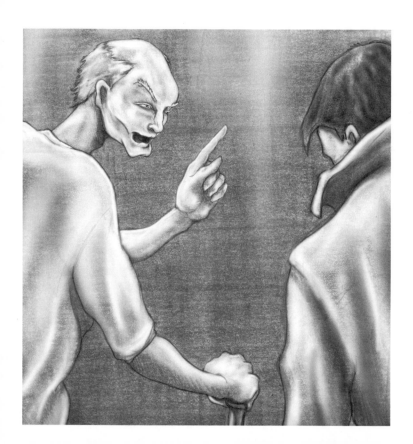

The Old Man:
It is in your eyes. You can not hide that.

The Dark Man:
If you must know, I am thinking of the past. Someone I lost.

The Old Man:
The girl. I know that you loved her.

The Dark Man:
Yes, Astrid. The Shadow Masters took her. I think about her all the time.

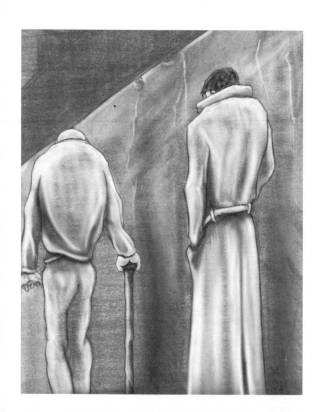

The Old Man:
> This is really hurting you, I
> see that.
>
> I did not want to tell you
> this. But I see that you
> need to know.

The Dark Man:
> Tell me. I am ready to
> listen.

The Old Man:
> She is still alive. The
> Shadow Masters have
> brought her to this city.

The Dark Man:
> Do you know where she is?
> Tell me.

The Old Man:
> There is a girl. She is dying.
> She can see things that
> are hidden.

The Dark Man:
> Will she tell me where
> Astrid is?

The Old Man:
> Take the magic stone. It
> will show her that you can
> be trusted.

Narrator:
> In a dark alley nearby, two Shadow Masters have heard everything.

Shadow Master 1:
> We can use the girl to set a trap for the Dark Man.

Shadow Master 2:
> With him dead, we will no longer have to fear the Old Man.

3

Act Three:
The Dying Girl

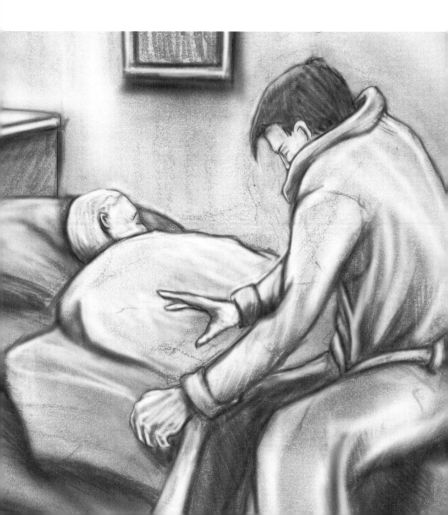

Narrator:
> The Dark Man has found the dying girl.

Dying girl:
> Welcome, Dark Man.

The Dark Man:
> How did you know I was here?

Dying girl:
> You carry the magic stone. I sense it near me.

Dying girl:
I can tell you where to find the girl you seek.

The Dark Man:
Then please tell me.

Dying girl:
I will. But you will be in great danger.

The Dark Man:
Tell me. I am not afraid.

4

Act Four:
In the Factory

Narrator:
The Dark Man has come to a factory making guns.

Narrator:
A Shadow Master holds Astrid.

Shadow Master 1:
The Dark Man has come to save you.

Astrid:
His name is David.

Shadow Master 1:
Names do not matter. Call out to him.

Astrid:
David, watch out! It's a trap!

Shadow Master 1:
It's too late to help him.

The Dark Man:
Astrid! Is it you?

Narrator:
A demon leaps out of the darkness.

The Dark Man:
Prepare to die. I have killed demons before.

Demon:
I am stronger than the ones you have killed.

 Narrator:
Astrid watches the fight.

 Astrid:
David, be careful.

 Shadow Master 1:
You should forget about him.

 Shadow Master 2:
Now come with us.

Narrator:
> The Dark Man throws the
> demon into molten steel.

The Dark Man:
> You might be strong, but
> the magic stone is
> stronger!

Demon:
> I'm dying!

Narrator:
> The Dark Man sees that Astrid is gone.

The Dark Man:
> Astrid! Astrid! Where are you?

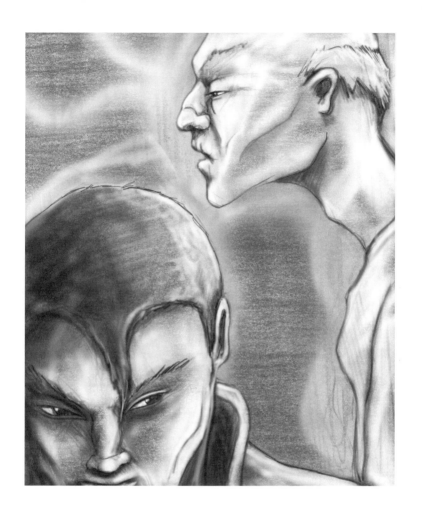

Narrator:
    The Dark Man goes to see
    the Old Man.

The Old Man:
I am sorry that you were not able to save Astrid.

The Dark Man:
They took her away as I was killing the demon.

The Old Man:
You will find her again.

The Dark Man:
> I shall never stop looking.

More **Dark Man** books:

Stories

Plays